MORE Dykes To Watch Out For

by Alison Bechdel

Firebrand Books
Ithaca, New York

Book and cover design by Alison Bechdel and Betsy Bayley

Printed in the United States by McNaughton & Gunn

Library of Congress Card No: 88-7096

Library of Congress Cataloging-in Publication Data

Bechdel, Alison, 1960–
   More dykes to watch out for / by Alison Bechdel.

      1. Lesbianism—United States—Caricatures and cartoons.
2. Lesbians—United States—Caricatures and cartoons.   I. Title.
HQ75.6.U5B423   1988   741.5'973—dc19   88-6892
ISBN 0–932379–46–X
ISBN 0–932379–45–1 (pbk.)

5

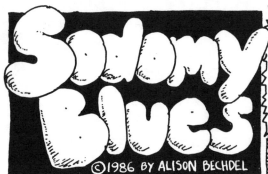

Sodomy Blues

©1986 BY ALISON BECHDEL

JUST WHEN YOU THOUGHT IT WAS **ALMOST** SAFE TO COME OUT OF THE CLOSET...

..TO ENGAGE IN ANY SEX ACT INVOLVING THE **SEX ORGANS** (PANT! PANT!) OF ONE PERSON AND THE **MOUTH** OR **ANUS** (DROOL) OF ANOTHER IS **UNCONSTITUTIONAL** AND **REVOLTING !!**

CHIEF SUPREME JERK

I THOUGHT SODOMY WAS HAVING SEX WITH A **FUNDAMENTALIST**..

HOW ANTE-DILUVIAN!

WHAT DOES IT ALL **MEAN** ?

WILL OUR SEX LIVES ONCE AGAIN BECOME **CLANDESTINE & GUILT-RIDDEN** ?

LOOK, I'D **LOVE** TO BUT I CAN'T **RISK** IT! FIDO'S LICENSE IS EXPIRED AND YOU NEVER KNOW WHEN THE **DOG CATCHER** MIGHT POP IN !

AND ON THE BEDROOM BEAT...

THEY'RE **STILL** AT SECOND BASE, AL! THIS COULD TAKE ALL **NIGHT!**

WARRANT PARKING VIOLAT..

..THEN AFTER WE OCCUPY THE **CAPITOL** BUILDING, WE ANCHOR THE **60 FOOT** INFLATABLE **TONGUE** FROM THE TOP OF THE DOME...

REALLY, CLAUDIA. LET'S GET **SERIOUS**.

IT'S NO LAUGHING MATTER! LET'S TAKE IT TO THE STATES!

6

FESTIVAL HELL

©1986 BY ALISON BECHDEL

EARLY ONE MORNING AT A PROMINENT WOMEN'S MUSIC FESTIVAL...

HONEY! WAKE UP! I JUST HAD THE MOST AWFUL NIGHTMARE!

Z

WE WERE HERE AT THE FESTIVAL, BUT IT WAS ALL DIFFERENT!

MM-HM

"FIRST, I WAS STANDING IN A LINE FOR HOURS, STARVING. WHEN I FINALLY GOT TO THE FRONT, THEY WERE FEEDING US BIRDSEED!

PURINA CANARY CHOW 50 LBS

"...THEN, I WANTED TO BUY AN EARRING, BUT THE CRAFTSWOMEN WOULD ONLY TAKE MAJOR CREDIT CARDS!

No PLASTIC? FORGET IT.

VISA

"AND MY GYM TEACHER FROM 9TH GRADE WAS THERE! SHE MADE ME DO 3 LAPS AROUND THE LAND FOR FORGETTING MY UNIFORM!

UH... THE CAT THREW UP ON IT?

POOR BABY.

WAIT, IT GETS MUCH WORSE. ALL MY EX-LOVERS WERE THERE! EVERY WOMAN I'VE EVER SLEPT WITH! GODDESS, IT WAS TERRIFYING!

"THEY WERE ALL HAVING A SUPPORT GROUP ABOUT ME!

HYPERSENSITIVE?! SHE ONCE SULKED FOR WEEKS BECAUSE I DIDN'T NOTICE HER HAIRCUT!

YEAH... SHE WAS ALWAYS OVER-REACTING!

YOU SAID IT!

HA! YOU DON'T KNOW THE HALF OF IT, SISTER!...

LISTEN, HONEY. IT WAS ONLY A DREAM! NOW, LET'S GET UP.

PENELOPE! WHAT A SURPRISE! WHEN WAS IT... THE SUMMER OF '79, WHEN WE CAME HERE TOGETHER?! HOW'S YOUR MOTHER?!

SHRIEK!!

WELL! YOU ALWAYS DID OVERREACT!

7

OH NO! IT'S...

INTERNALIZED HOMO-PHOBIA!

© 1986 BY ALISON BECHDEL

IT'S **SAD** BUT **TRUE**! NO MATTER HOW WELL-ADJUSTED YOU ARE, EVERY NOW AND THEN THAT **NAGGING LITTLE VOICE** POPS UP!

OF COURSE, YOUR **LESBIAN IDENTITY** ALWAYS **WINS**,... BUT WHAT A **WASTE** OF **ENERGY**!

One method of quieting the homophobic voice is by **DIRECT CONFRONTATION**.

ESTELLE! WHAT WOULD YOUR **MOTHER** THINK?!

AW, GO **MASTURBATE** WITH YER **MICROWAVE**, YA PRISSY, PRE-PROGRAMMED **POLLYANNA**!

To SILENCE IT **PERMANENTLY** REQUIRES CONSTANT VIGILANCE,...

DON'T HOLD HANDS! DO YOU WANT TO GET US **HARASSED**?!

GO ON! TAKE HER **HAND**! LET'S SHOW THESE POOR **ROBOTS** WHAT A COUPLA HAPPY **LESBIANS** LOOK LIKE!

... STEADFASTNESS AGAINST **TEMPTATION**,...

I **WISH** YOU'D GET A **CAREER** AND A **CREDIT CARD**! THIS MARGINAL EXISTENCE IS SO **STRESSFUL**!

LISTEN, ESTELLE! WE MIGHT NOT HAVE A **VCR**, BUT AT LEAST WE HAVE OUR **FREEDOM**!

... AND MAYBE THERAPY.

A LITTLE 'TOTAL WOMAN' WITH A PITCHFORK?

9

Butch & FEMME

© 1986 BY ALISON BECHDEL

CURIOUS LITTLE **TERMS**, AREN'T THEY? **SOME** WOMEN ARE **DISDAINFUL** OF THEM.

OOH, YUCK. **ROLE**-PLAYING! WE'RE **ABOVE** ALL THAT!

SOME WOMEN HAVE MADE THEM INTO A **SCIENCE**.

NO, NO... JANET IS DEFINITELY YOUR TYPICAL **BUTCHY FEMME**.

FACE IT. NO MATTER **HOW** POLITICALLY CORRECT YOU ARE, THERE ARE ALL THESE **ROLES** LURKING ABOUT, JUST **WAITING** TO ENSNARE THE UNSUSPECTING VICTIM.

IT'S CALLED A **SKIRT**. I FIND IT **COMFORTABLE**. OKAY?

UGH... COULD YOU TRY THIS?

WHY **SURE**, DARLING.

MAYBE YOU TRY TO **FIGHT** THEM.

MAYBE YOU SORT OF GET **INTO** THEM.

BUT THE TRUE **GLORY** OF THE **LESBIAN EXPERIENCE** IS REVEALED BY OUR THRILLING AND EXTRAORDINARY **VERSATILITY** IN TIMES OF CRISIS.

Cold Turkey

© 1986 BY ALISON BECHDEL

THIS YEAR, IN OPPOSITION TO MY **WASP** HERITAGE, I'M REFUSING TO TAKE PART IN OPPRESSIVE HOLIDAYS.

THANKSGIVING IS JUST A HYPOCRITICAL **WHITE**WASHING OF THE **GENOCIDE** OF AMERICAN INDIANS.

CHRISTMAS IS A CAPITALIST CONSPIRACY OF CONSPICUOUS CONSUMPTION,...

...CRAMMED DOWN OUR COLLECTIVE THROAT, REGARDLESS OF OUR INDIVIDUAL RELIGIONS!

YOU SAID ALL THIS **LAST** YEAR, JULIA! BUT WHERE **WERE** YOU ON THANKSGIVING? OVEREATING IN FRONT OF A **TELEVISION** SET!

13

14

15

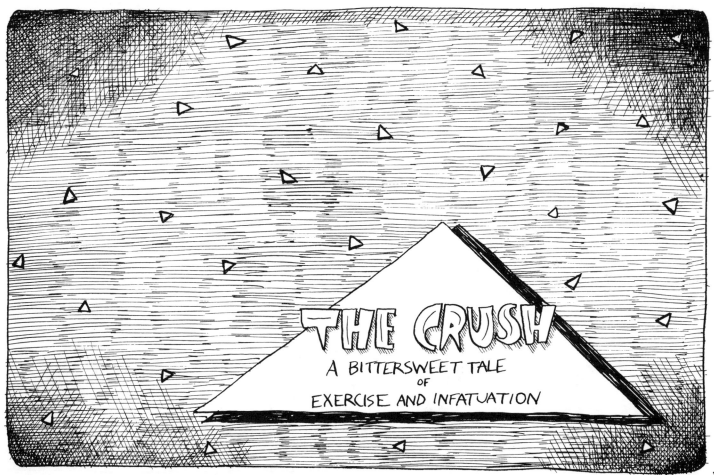

The CRUSH

IN RETROSPECT, I WAS **RIPE** FOR IT. IT WAS **SPRING** AND I HADN'T HAD A DATE, LET ALONE **SEX**, IN MONTHS. I WAS TOO BUSY **SUBLIMATING**.

FIVE KARATE CLASSES A WEEK TOOK A LOT OUT OF ME. ANY EXTRA ENERGY I HAD WAS SPENT KEEPING MY **UNIFORM** LAUNDERED.

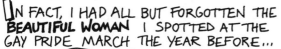

IN FACT, I HAD ALL BUT FORGOTTEN THE **BEAUTIFUL WOMAN** I SPOTTED AT THE GAY PRIDE MARCH THE YEAR BEFORE...

IT WAS UNUSUAL FOR ME TO BE SO COMPLETELY **STRUCK** BY A STRANGER... BUT SOMETHING ABOUT HER **MOVED** ME.

NOW, HOWEVER, IT WAS A YEAR LATER, AND I WAS SUBLIMATING **HARD.**

THIRTY-ONE! THIRTY-TWO!

I WAS COUNTING THE DAYS UNTIL THE ANNUAL **WOMEN'S MARTIAL ARTS TRAINING CAMP** IN JUNE.

IT WAS A GREAT EVENT. HUNDREDS OF **AMAZONS** GATHERED FROM ALL OVER THE COUNTRY, AND EVEN FROM **EUROPE**, TO STUDY AND TRAIN TOGETHER FOR **FOUR GLORIOUS DAYS**. I WENT WITH MY TEACHER AND SOME WOMEN FROM MY SCHOOL.

AND THEN, I **SAW** HER! I DON'T HAVE A VERY GOOD MEMORY FOR FACES, BUT I KNEW IT WAS **HER**, THE WOMAN FROM THE MARCH!! I STARTED TO FEEL **WEAK**. ALL THOSE MONTHS OF PUSH-UPS AND SIT-UPS, AND NOW I HAD SUDDENLY **TURNED** TO **JELLY**!

THE FIRST EVENING, ALL **400** OF US HAD A CLASS TOGETHER IN THE GYM. I POSITIONED MYSELF **NEAR** HER, BUT NOT **TOO** NEAR...

I WAS IN TORMENT. I KNEW I HAD TO **TALK** TO HER, BUT I WAS STRANGELY **PARALYZED** BY THE PROSPECT.

I DIDN'T SLEEP WELL THAT NIGHT.

The next afternoon, we were in a class together outside. I **surprised** myself.

NEED A PARTNER?

HEY, UM... UH... DO YOU WANNA BE **PARTNERS**?

PARTNERS?

YUP.

To my horror and delight, she **agreed**. She tossed her damp gi top off on the grass before we began.

OMIGOD... THOSE **SHOULDERS!**

HOT OUT, HUH?

The instructor told us to deliver **slow motion** attacks to specific targets on our partners, making **gentle** but **firm** contact.

The first time I **touched** her was a slow blow to her sweaty jaw.

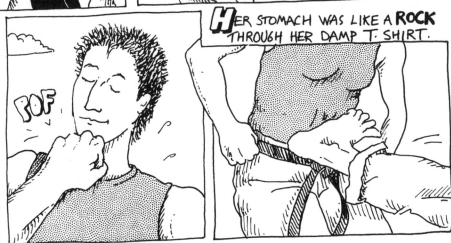

POF

Her stomach was like a **rock** through her damp t-shirt.

AFTER THE CLASS, SHE ASKED FOR A **DRINK** FROM MY WATER BOTTLE.

WE TALKED ON OUR WAY BACK TO THE GYM. SHE TOLD ME SHE JUST GRADUATED FROM COLLEGE. **IVY LEAGUE.** SHE ROWED **CREW** AND WAS GOING TO BE A **DOCTOR.**

WHAT A **BLUEBLOOD**... JEEZ, I'M SUCH A **BUM!**

...I WAS GOING TO GO TO LAW SCHOOL, BUT I CHANGED MY MIND...

I WAS VERY **IMPRESSIONABLE** IN THOSE DAYS...

I WAS A GONER, BUT I TRIED TO BE COOL.

SEE YA

SOLAR PLEXUS ACHE

NORMALLY A VERY BIG EATER, I FOUND THAT I HAD **COMPLETELY** LOST MY **APPETITE!**

WHATSA **MATTER** WITH **YOU?**

I BEGAN TO ANNOY MY FRIENDS.

OH MY **GOD!** THERE SHE **IS!** ISN'T SHE **MAGNIFICENT?**

OK, OK! SHE'S **CUTE** ALREADY!

THE NEXT MORNING, I WAS OUT RUNNING AS THE SUN CAME UP. SHE FELL INTO STEP BESIDE ME.

HI!

OH! GOOD **MORNING!**

SHE WAS A **BEAUTIFUL** ATHLETE, AND TALKED **EASILY** AS WE RAN.

...PULLED HAMSTRINGS... SPRINTS... MILE A DAY...

WE BREAKFASTED TOGETHER. I **STILL** WASN'T HUNGRY. WE TALKED ABOUT BEING **MISTAKEN** FOR **BOYS.**

CONVENIENT. SOMETIMES.

...EXCEPT WHEN THEY CALL YOU **FAGGOT.**

ON THE WAY BACK TO THE DORMS, I WAS FEELING MORE **COMFORTABLE** WITH HER...

SO, HOW **OLD** ARE YOU?

THEN A STRANGE THING HAPPENED...

22.

YEAH? ME TOO! WHAT MONTH WERE YOU BORN?

SEPTEMBER.

ME TOO! WHAT **DAY?**

THE TENTH.

WE REMARKED ON THE COINCIDENCE FOR A WHILE, AND THEN AN EVEN **STRANGER** THING HAPPENED!

I SAW YOU AT THE **GAY PRIDE** MARCH LAST YEAR.

NO! YOU'RE **KIDDING!** THAT'S **MY** BIRTHDAY!

NO **SHIT!**

I DISGUISED MY **SWOON** WITH AN ATTEMPTED HANDSTAND.

I SAW **YOU** THERE TOO!

THEN, OVERCOME WITH SELF-CONSCIOUSNESS, I CHANGED THE SUBJECT COMPLETELY.

SO, WHAT DID YOU **MAJOR** IN?

WE STOOD THERE TALKING AS THE SUN DRIED THE GRASS. SHE SPOKE WITH A FAINT **DRAWL**. HER EYES WERE **VIOLET**, AND SHE SMELLED OF COCONUT OIL.

...THE CELLULAR CONSTRUCTION OF FUNGI...

WOW, REALLY?

26

I WAS **MESMERIZED** BY HER **BICEPS** AND THE **VEIN** THAT RAN ACROSS HER SHOULDER. HER SKIN WAS LIKE POLISHED **MARBLE**.

I WAS **LOST** TO **REASON**. I BELIEVED IN **FATE** AT THE TIME.

WE WERE PARTNERS TOGETHER IN THE **LAST CLASS** OF THE WEEKEND.

IT WAS A VERY **HOT** MORNING. AT ONE POINT SHE **CHANGED** HER **SHIRT**. I WAS TOO OVERCOME TO EVEN WATCH.

WE WERE LEARNING THE BASICS OF A **STRANGE, BRAZILIAN** MARTIAL ART. I COULD SMELL HER **COCONUT** OIL. I WAS **ECSTATIC**.

AFTER THE CLASS, WE ALL GATHERED FOR A GROUP PHOTO.

I LOOKED FOR HER TO SAY GOODBYE, BUT SHE HAD **DISAPPEARED**.

THERE WAS NO SIGN OF HER **ANYWHERE**. **CRUSHED**, I REALIZED I DIDN'T EVEN KNOW HER **LAST NAME!**
I DIDN'T WANT TO LEAVE. THE DRIVE BACK TO THE CITY WAS **EXCRUCIATING**.

I DIDN'T WASH MY DIRTY GI FOR **DAYS**. IT SMELLED LIKE **GRASS** AND **FRESH AIR** AND **SWEAT**...

— SNIFF

AND **POSSIBLY**, VERY **FAINTLY**, OF COCONUT OIL.

29

One ★ Enchanted Evening

© 1987 BY ALISON BECHDEL

I'M **TIRED** OF BEING **CELIBATE**, LO! I HAVEN'T HAD **SEX** IN... 8 MONTHS!

"**CELIBATE**?!" YOU MAKE IT SOUND LIKE IT WAS A CONSCIOUS **CHOICE**. ADMIT IT, MO. THE OPPORTUNITY JUST HASN'T ARISEN.

OKAY, OKAY! I ADMIT IT. BUT IT'S SO **HARD** TO MEET **WOMEN**, AND BESIDES, I HAVE SUCH **HIGH STANDARDS**!

YEAH. RIGHT. SO WHAT WAS WRONG WITH THE CUTE **ACCOUNTANT**?

SHE WASN'T **POLITICAL** ENOUGH. **BESIDES**, SHE WAS ALREADY **INVOLVED**.

WHAT ABOUT THE WOMAN IN YOUR KARATE CLASS YOU WERE SO HOT FOR?

SHE WASN'T **INTELLECTUAL** ENOUGH. BESIDES, SHE DOESN'T SLEEP WITH OTHER KARATE STUDENTS. MATTER OF **POLICY**.

RIGHT... WHAT ABOUT **NAOMI** FROM THE **FOOD CO-OP?**

ARE YOU CRAZY? I'M WAY TOO **CRUSHED** OUT! I CAN'T EVEN ASK HER WHERE THE **BULGHUR** IS WITHOUT **HYPERVENTILATING!** NO... THAT KIND OF THING NEVER WORKS.

WELL... WHAT ABOUT **ME?**

VERY FUNNY, LOIS. YOU **KNOW** WE COULD NEVER HAVE AN **AFFAIR!** I HAVE TO FEEL **ROMANTIC** ABOUT SOMEONE BEFORE I **SLEEP** WITH THEM!

I KNOW, I KNOW. MAKING OUT WITH ME WOULD JUST BE INDULGING YOUR **BASE, LOWER NATURE,** RIGHT?

WELL... YEAH. **SORT** OF...

THANKS, MO. I'LL TAKE THAT AS A **COMPLIMENT.** LUCKY FOR ME, THOUGH, I DON'T **BELIEVE** IN "LOWER NATURE!"

WHERE ARE YOU **GOING?**

I HAVE A DATE FOR SOME **HOT & HEAVY UNROMANCE** WITH **NAOMI!** SHE WANTS TO TRY MY **FAMOUS SEAWEED AVOCADO PATÉ!** CIAO, BELLA!

RATZ! I NEVER HAVE ANY FUN!

IS MO A HOPELESSLY ROMANTIC IDEALIST, TRAPPED IN THE **HARD-NOSED, FAST-PACED** WHIRLWIND OF MODERN LESBIAN LIFE? OR IS SHE JUST A **DRAG?** STAY TOONED!

MO & LO in... the STUDIO

© 1987 BY ALISON BECHDEL

MO'S LIFE HAS TAKEN A **TURN** FOR THE **WORSE**. STILL WITHOUT A LOVER, SHE HAS ALSO LOST HER **JOB** AND BECOME THE VICTIM OF A REGRETTABLE **HAIRCUT!**

AT LEAST IT'S **WINTER**. I CAN KEEP THIS HAT ON TILL MY **HAIR** GROWS BACK.

UNEMPLOY

A RESOURCEFUL WOMAN, SHE DOES NOT GIVE IN TO DESPAIR, BUT KEEPS HERSELF BUSY.

②

BUT WHEN **NO MAIL** ARRIVES, EXCEPT FOR A **REJECTION** LETTER FROM A PROMINENT LESBIAN·FEMINIST **LITERARY** JOUR-NAL...EVEN OUR **HEROINE'S** NATURE IS RESILIENT TESTED!

SHRED!

SHE TURNS TO HER FAITHFUL FRIEND **LOIS** FOR SUPPORT.

I'M SO **DEPRESSED!** HOW'M I EVER GOING TO GET A **JOB** LET ALONE A **GIRLFRIEND**, WITH THIS HAIRCUT?! I LOOK LIKE A **TRANSSEXUAL MARINE!**

MO, RELAX! YOU'RE GETTING ALL WORKED UP.

OF COURSE I'M GETTING WORKED UP! I'M **ANXIOUS** AND **TENSE** BECAUSE I HAVEN'T HAD **SEX** IN TEN MONTHS!

HIGH ANXIETY

©1987 BY ALISON BECHDEL

ONE NIGHT AFTER KARATE CLASS...

DON'T YOU SEE THE **IRONY** OF YOUR SITUATION, MO? YOU MIGHT BE MISERABLE NOT HAVING A JOB...

BUT WHAT'S **THAT** COMPARED WITH THE MISERY OF **HAVING** ONE? WHY DON'T YOU COME OVER FOR DINNER TONIGHT? I TOLD TONI YOU WOULD.

SURE, CLARICE.

SNAP! SNAP!

HI ANTONIA.

WELL, IF IT AIN'T THE **KARATE KIDS!**

STILL **JOB HUNTING,** MO?

GROAN

RIGHT.

SHE'S KINDA **ANXIOUS & DEPRESSED.** LET'S TRY AND **CHEER** HER UP!

OVER THE LENTIL STEW...

GEE, MO... SINCE YOU'RE **COLLECTING UNEMPLOYMENT,** WHY DON'T YOU JUST TAKE **TIME OUT** TO DO SOMETHING YOU REALLY **LIKE?!** **ENJOY** YOUR **FREEDOM!**

Mo & Clarice in... the HOAX

© 1987 BY ALISON BECHDEL

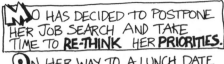

MO HAS DECIDED TO POSTPONE HER JOB SEARCH AND TAKE TIME TO **RE-THINK** HER **PRIORITIES.**

ON HER WAY TO A LUNCH DATE WITH HER **EX-LOVER,** CLARICE ...

JADED... I'VE BECOME. SO **JADED.** WHERE DID ALL MY REVOLUTIONARY **FERVOR** GO?

SCUFF SCUFF (4)

I REMEMBER WHEN CLARICE AND I CAME OUT TOGETHER IN COLLEGE... WE WERE SO **EXCITED,** SO **RADICAL,** SO **COMMITTED** TO **DISMANTLING** THE **PATRIARCHY!** CLARICE STILL **IS**... BUT SOMEWHERE ALONG THE LINE, **I** STOPPED FIGHTING...

BARBER SHOP

HEY, MO! SO HOW'S THE **PRIORITY CHECK** GOING?

PAINFULLY. HOW'S LAW SCHOOL?

SAME OLD SHIT. STUDYING MY ASS OFF.

CLARICE, I JUST WANT YOU TO KNOW HOW MUCH I **ADMIRE** YOU, PATIENTLY PLAYING THE **BOYS' GAMES** BY THE **BOYS' RULES,** WORKING FOR CHANGE **INSIDE** THE **SYSTEM**.. SLOWLY GAINING THE **POWER** TO REALLY **SHAKE** THINGS UP! **ATTACK** FROM **WITHIN**... THE OLE' **TROJAN HORSE** PLOY...

Y'KNOW, MO, I'M REALLY GETTING **INTO** MY **CORPORATE TAX** CLASS LATELY!

LISTEN... IF I WENT INTO **CORPORATE LAW,** I COULD MAKE $70,000 MY **FIRST YEAR** OUT OF SCHOOL...

WHAT?

Cafe Topaz

UH...JUST TO PAY BACK YOUR **LOANS**, **RIGHT?** THEN, AFTER A YEAR YOU'LL GO WORK FOR **LEGAL AID**, **RIGHT?**

WELL, I DUNNO... TONI AND I ARE THINKING OF BUYING A **HOUSE** AND HAVING **KIDS**... YOU NEED **MONEY** FOR THAT.

CLARICE! OLD **COMRADE!** WHAT ARE YOU **SAYING?!**

GODDESS **KNOWS**, US WOMEN OF COLOR HAVE A HARD ENOUGH TIME IN THIS COUNTRY... WHY SHOULDN'T I **ENJOY** THE FRUITS OF MY **LABORS?** GET A MICROWAVE, A VOLVO STATION WAGON...

CLARICE! I DIDN'T THINK IT COULD HAPPEN! **YOU**, OF ALL PEOPLE! MY **LAST HOPE!**

...PRIVATE SCHOOLS FOR THE KIDS,.. QUIET EVENINGS WITH TONI, PORING OVER OUR **STOCK PORTFOLIO**...

CLARICE! SNAP OUT OF IT! **JESUS**, WHERE ARE THOSE **DEPROGRAMMERS** WHEN YOU **NEED** ONE?!

MO, **RELAX!** I'M JUST PULLING YOUR **LEG!**

CLARICE THE **UNSWERVING!** THE ORIGINAL RADICAL LESBIAN FEMINIST **TERRORIST!** WHAT **HOPE** IS THERE FOR POOR WIMPS LIKE **ME** IF EVEN **YOU** HAVE KNUCKLED UNDER?!

MO, I **SAID** I WAS **KIDDING!** LIGHTEN **UP!**

I MAY AS WELL SEE IF THE **C.I.A.** IS HIRING!

UH...WHY DON'T I COME BACK LATER?

GOOD IDEA.

39

IT'S **MO** AGAIN! AND SHE'S HAVING...

NO SEX

© 1987 BY ALISON BECHDEL

LIFE PLODS ON FOR OUR AMOROUS HEROINE.

...HER EYES DARK WITH DESIRE, MONIQUE LICKED THE MELTED PAPAYA ICE CREAM FROM URSULA'S FINGERS. "I WANT YOU," WHISPERED URSULA HOARSELY, USING HER FREE HAND TO FUMBLE WITH THE ZIPPERS OF MONIQUE'S BLACK LEATHER FLIGHTSUIT...

VANILLA LEATHER LOVE

SIGH.

⑤

THE NEXT MORNING FINDS MO AT HER FAVORITE LESBO HANGOUT, **CAFE TOPAZ**...

..ALMOST A **YEAR** SINCE MY LAST SEXUAL ENCOUNTER, AND **STILL** NO SIGN OF MS. RIGHT...

MY **PENT-UP** EROTIC ENERGY IS DRIVING ME **CRAZY**... I'M ATTRACTED TO EVERY DYKE I **SEE**... THEY'RE ALL SO... SO **SEXY**...

THE WAY THEY LAUGH...

THE WAY THEY WALK...

THE WAY THEIR JEANS FIT...

40

41

the GOY

©1987 BY ALISON BECHDEL

YEAH, NAOMI AND I HAVE BEEN MESSING AROUND A LITTLE, BUT IT'S NOTHING SERIOUS... OH, BY THE WAY, SHE'S HAVING A **SEDER** FOR **PASSOVER** ON MONDAY... SHE TOLD ME TO **INVITE** YOU.

ME? LOIS, **I** CAN'T GO TO NAOMI'S SEDER! I STILL HAVE A **CRUSH** ON HER... AND BESIDES, I'M NOT **JEWISH**!

AW, C'MON, MO! CLARICE AND TONI WILL BE THERE! YOU WON'T BE THE ONLY GOY!

GOY? WHAT'S A **GOY**?

ANYONE WHO WOULD ASK THAT QUESTION IS A GOY, OK? SEE YOU MONDAY!

ON MONDAY, MO GETS A RIDE WITH CLARICE & TONI.

SO, LIKE, HAVE YOU GUYS EVER **BEEN** TO ONE OF THESE THINGS? WHAT IF I DO SOMETHING **DUMB**?

MO, **RELAX**. WE'RE GOING TO HAVE A GOOD **TIME**!

SHALOM, NAOMI!

CLARICE! TONI! SHALOM! COME ON IN! PUT YOUR FOOD ON THE TABLE...

HI, MO! WHADJA BRING?

UH... HI, NAOMI... I... UH... I BROUGHT SOME, UH... **RYE** BREAD. WITH **SEEDS**.

OH, MO, THAT'S SWEET! BUT WE ONLY EAT UNLEAVENED BREAD DURING PASSOVER!

OH.

DON'T WORRY! THERE'S PLENTY OF MATZAH! COME ON, EVERYBODY! LET'S SIT DOWN!

SHIT!

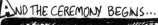

AND THE CEREMONY BEGINS...

MO GETS TO READ THE FOUR QUESTIONS.

WHY ON THIS NIGHT DO WE EAT MATZAH INSTEAD OF BREAD?

A LESBIAN HAGGADAH!

FOR ALL OF YOU WHO'VE NEVER BEEN TO A **SEDER**, LET ME **EXPLAIN** A LITTLE. PASSOVER IS A WONDERFUL TRADITION. TONIGHT WE CELEBRATE THE LIBERATION OF THE JEWS FROM **SLAVERY** IN **EGYPT**. THIS IS A RITUAL ABOUT OPPRESSION, AND RESISTANCE, AND FREEDOM, AND...

AND BY THE END OF THE EVENING, SHE'S ACTUALLY **ENJOYING** HERSELF!

PHARAOH'S ARMY GOT DROWN-DED! OH, MARY DONTCHA WEEP!

...SPRINGTIME, AND **LIFE!**

SMAK

CLAP CLAP

AWRIGHT! LIGHT THE CANDLES!

THAT WAS **GREAT!** I HAD A **REALLY** GOOD TIME! AND I ONLY DID **ONE** DUMB THING!

NOT **BAD**, FOR A GOY!

TOYOTA

ABOLISH APARTHEID

CO-OP WE OWN IT

U.S. OUT OF NICARAGUA

627·DYK

I ♥ ♀'s ♪

43

IT'S CLARICE & TONI! AND THEY'RE...

GETTING RESPECTABLE

© 1987 BY ALISON BECHDEL

ON THE PHONE WITH **MO** ONE MORNING...

...BLAH, BLAH...WHINE... NO GIRLFRIEND... NO SEX.. WHINE... BLAH, BLAH...

I KNOW, MO. BUT IT'S SPRING! THINGS WILL START HAPPENING AGAIN!

BYE, DARLING!

GRAPE GRAVEL

I GUESS SO... SO HOW ARE YOU AND TONI?

JUST **GREAT!** YOU KNOW, I DON'T THINK I'VE EVER **BEEN** SO HAPPY! IN FACT,...

THAT'S NICE. WELL, I HAVE TO GO READ THE PERSONALS NOW. THANKS FOR LISTENING, CLARICE!

ON CAMPUS THAT DAY...

IT'S GREAT TO **SEE** YOU, CLARICE! IT'S BEEN **MONTHS!** SO, ARE YOU & TONI STILL TOGETHER?

UH... LAST I HEARD, WE WERE.

LATER IN THE AFTERNOON...

...MY OTHER GIRLFRIEND ANGELA IS KIND OF UPTIGHT ABOUT ME SEEING NAOMI. ANGELA'S A REAL **LINEAR** THINKER. SHE CAN'T SEEM TO **TRANSCEND** THE **MONOGAMOUS MINDSET.**

GEE, LO. THAT'S ROUGH.

44

FINALLY, BACK AT THE RANCH...

JUNE! I'M HO-OME!

IN HERE, WARD!

TONI, AM I STILL YOUR ONE AND ONLY?

I THINK SO. WHY?

I WAS AFRAID MAYBE SINCE THIS MORNING YOU DECIDED THAT MONOGAMY WAS TOO LINEAR, AND SO YOU TRANSCENDED IT.

WELL... IT IS KIND OF UNCOOL... BUT I THINK YOU'RE STUCK WITH ME.

WHY IS IT SO UNCOOL? WE DON'T GET ANY CREDIT, TONI! WHEN I RUN INTO SOMEONE I HAVEN'T SEEN IN A WHILE, IT'S ALWAYS "SO, ARE YOU TWO STILL TOGETHER?" LIKE THEY EXPECT US TO BREAK UP!

AND NO ONE WANTS TO HEAR ABOUT HOW HAPPY I AM WITH YOU. THEY'RE ONLY INTERESTED IN ROMANTIC STRIFE!

SO, NOW WE NEED A SUPPORT GROUP FOR HAPPY COUPLES?

YOU KNOW WHAT I MEAN! I DON'T EXPECT ANYTHING FROM THE STRAIGHT WORLD, BUT YOU'D THINK AT LEAST OTHER DYKES WOULD VALIDATE OUR RELATIONSHIP!

WELL... STRAIGHT COUPLES GET RESPECT WHEN THEY MARRY. MAYBE WE NEED TO MAKE SOME KIND OF SYMBOLIC AFFIRMATION OF OUR COMMITMENT TO ONE ANOTHER!

YOU MEAN...

YES! LET'S OPEN A JOINT CHECKING ACCOUNT!

OH, DARLING! BUT THIS IS SO SUDDEN!

45

ANGST IN RIGHT FIELD

8

©1987 BY ALISON BECHDEL

IT'S SOFTBALL SEASON AGAIN, AND MO'S HAVING A TOUCH OF **WELTSCHMERZ** IN THE LAST INNING...

IT'S SO PEACEFUL OUT HERE...

YOU'D NEVER SUSPECT THAT SOMEWHERE POLITICAL PRISONERS ARE BEING **TORTURED**, PEOPLE ARE **STARVING**, **CHEMICALS** ARE SPILLING, **MISSILES** ARE PILING UP... NOPE! HERE IN THE HEART OF THE BEAST, EVERYTHING'S JUST **HUNKY DORY!**

SOUTH AFRICA, CENTRAL AMERICA, AND THE MIDDLE EAST ARE ALL FAR AWAY. WE CAN WATCH THEM SAFELY ON THE **NEWS** EVERY NIGHT...

AND WHEN SOMETHING GETS TOO CLOSE TO HOME, THE NETWORKS FIND WAYS TO KEEP IT PALATABLE AND UNINFORMATIVE...

LIKE CALLING **OLIVER NORTH** AND HIS HENCHMEN 'KEY PLAYERS' IN THE IRAN-CONTRA DEAL, INSTEAD OF SOMETHING **LESS POSITIVE** LIKE CRIMINALLY INSANE HYPERMILITARY @*#⊕☆!* WARMONGERS!'

SMEK!

RESUME OF THE DAMNED

THANKS FOR COMING OVER, LOIS! MY **UNEMPLOYMENT** RUNS OUT IN A COUPLE WEEKS AND I GOTTA GET MY **RESUME** TOGETHER.

NO PROBLEM, MO OLD PAL! I'M GOOD AT THIS KIND OF THING!

END APARTHEID

DIVEST NOW

9

OKAY. LET'S START WITH YOUR LAST JOB.

PROOFREADER AND PRODUCTION ASSISTANT FOR THE NOW-DEFUNCT **GAYLY FORWARD NEWS**

..AND BEFORE THAT?

OFFICE ASSISTANT AT THE **ABORTION RIGHTS ACTION COUNCIL**.

UH...OKAY. AND BEFORE THAT?

DELIVERY-PERSON FOR THE **COMMON WOMON** (THAT'S WITH AN 'O') BREAD COLLECTIVE.

HM...THIS ISN'T SOUNDING TOO PROMISING..HOW ABOUT **VOLUNTEER** WORK?

WELL, I HAVE GOOD **EDITING** SKILLS FROM MY TWO YEARS ON THE STAFF OF THE **LESBIAN RAG**...

I GOT EXPERIENCE DOING **COUNSELING** WHEN I VOLUNTEERED AT THE BATTERED WOMEN'S SHELTER...

AND I HAVE **FACILITATING** AND **ORGANIZING** SKILLS FROM PLANNING DEMONSTRATIONS WITH THE **CLARA LEMLICH** MEMORIAL AFFINITY GROUP AND **GRAFFITI GUERRILLAS!**

MO, MO, MO... HAVEN'T YOU DONE ANYTHING LESS, UH... LESS **PROGRESSIVE?**

WHADDAYA MEAN?

I MEAN, WHO'S GONNA HIRE YOU WITH A RESUMÉ LIKE **THIS?** C'MON, MO, **THINK!** YOU MUST HAVE DONE **SOME** WORK WHICH HAD **LITTLE** OR **NO** SOCIALLY REDEEMING **VALUE!**

WELL **JEEZ**, LOIS! I'M NOT **TRYING** TO GET A JOB WITH THE **STATE DEPARTMENT!**

OKAY, FINE! **BE** DOWNWARDLY MOBILE! **GET** ANOTHER LOW-PAYING JOB IN SOME IDEALISTIC, GOODY-TWO-SHOES ALTERNATIVE ORGANIZATION! SEE IF **I** CARE!

BY THE WAY, WE NEED ANOTHER **CASHIER** AT THE WOMEN'S BOOKSTORE. $5 AN HOUR, NO BENEFITS. WHY DON'T YOU COME BY DURING MY SHIFT TOMORROW AND APPLY?

WHAT A PAL!

49

A LESSON in GRAVITY

©1987 BY ALISON BECHDEL

As we wait to hear whether MO has been hired as a cashier at **MADWIMMIN BOOKS**, we turn our attention to **ANOTHER** of her many problems!

(10)

WE FIND MO & CLARICE LIMBERING UP BEFORE KARATE CLASS...

MY SUPPLE YOUNG BODY IS SLOWLY WASTING AWAY FROM **LACK** OF **USE**, CLARICE! WHAT AM I GONNA **DO**? I NEED A **LOVE** INTEREST!

MO, YOU'RE **TRYING** TOO HARD! PEOPLE PICK THAT UP AND IT SCARES THEM OFF!

WHY? I'M A NICE CATCH! SHY BUT **PASSIONATE**, POLITICALLY **AWARE**, SKILLED IN **SELF-DEFENSE**!

NAH... THAT HAS NOTHING TO DO WITH IT. WOMEN WILL RUN AWAY FROM THE MOST **SOCIALLY CONSCIOUS**, MOST **EMOTIONALLY TOGETHER**, MOST **HOT-LOOKING** DYKE IN THE WORLD IF THEY SENSE SHE'S LOOKING FOR A **LOVER**!

I WOULDN'T! WHERE **IS** SHE?

YES, YOU WOULD. IT'S A LAW OF **GRAVITY**. THE MORE **DESPERATE** YOU ARE, THE MORE **REPEL** WOMEN! YOU

WHAT ARE YOU **TALKING** ABOUT, CLARICE? REMEMBER OUR SOPHOMORE YEAR IN COLLEGE? WE WERE SO **DESPERATE** FOR **EACH OTHER** WE FLUNKED EVERYTHING EXCEPT OUR **WOMEN'S STUDIES** CLASS!

OH, MO... THAT WAS **DIFFERENT.** IT WAS ALL **NEW** TO US THEN. YOU'RE MORE EXPERIENCED NOW. AND YOU'RE NOT GOING TO FIND A LOVER UNTIL YOU GET TO THE POINT WHERE YOU REALLY **AREN'T LOOKING** FOR ONE.

BUT I NEED TO HAVE **SEX! SOON!** I'M **TIRED** OF **CREATIVE MASTURBATION!**

TIRED OF IT! I'LL BET YOU HAVEN'T TRIED IT WITH **JELLO** YET!

I HAVE **TOO.** YOU TOLD ME THAT ONE **MONTHS** AGO.

MO, LISTEN. I KNOW YOU'RE HAVING A ROUGH TIME, BUT IT'S HARD BEING **SUPPORTIVE** AND **ENCOURAGING** WHEN ALL YOU DO IS **WHINE!**

WHINE? ME? CLARICE, I DON'T **WHINE** ... DO I?

☐S MO GOING TOO **FAR?** IS SHE STARTING TO REPEL HER **FRIENDS** AS **WELL** AS POTENTIAL **LOVERS?** WILL SHE GET HER **ACT** TOGETHER? BEAR WITH HER A LITTLE LONGER, AND **MAYBE** YOU'LL **FIND OUT!**

I DUNNO, LOIS... I MEAN, PEOPLE ARE DYING OF **MALNUTRITION** AND YOU GO OUT AND BUY A **VCR**...

I'M SO EXCITED!

JUST ONE MORE **TECHNO-TOY** TO KEEP US COMPLACENT, CONSUMPTION-ORIENTED, AND **DISEMPOWERED!**

YEAH.

YOU **THINK** IT'S JUST ENTERTAINMENT. BUT IT'S A **DISEASE**, LOIS! AN **INSIDIOUS**, SOUL-DESTROYING, HUMANITY-SAPPING **CANCER!**

HAND ME THE SCREWDRIVER.

INSTRUCTIONS

IT'S A HETEROPATRIARCHAL **PLOT**, LOIS! YOU BUY THEIR VCR, AND **THEN** YOU START WATCHING THEIR **MOVIES!**

I MEAN, I CAN COUNT ON **ONE HAND** THE FILMS I'VE SEEN THAT DIDN'T **SOMEHOW** MANAGE TO OFFEND MY LESBIAN-FEMINIST SENSIBILITIES!

A TIP O' THE PEN TO NETT HART.

WHEN WE GET TO THE PART WHERE THEY **KISS** IN THE **RAIN**, CAN WE PLAY IT **BACK**?

AS MANY TIMES AS YOU **WANT**.

DO YOU WANNA SEE **DESERT HEARTS** OR THIS **WHOOPI GOLDBERG** MOVIE?

LOIS, YOU CAN ONLY WATCH DESERT HEARTS **SO MANY TIMES!** NEXT THING YOU KNOW YOU'LL BE BRINGING HOME **CLINT EASTWOOD** FLICKS!

DESERT HEARTS IT IS! WILL YOU PUH-LEASE SIT DOWN AND **RELAX**?

THE CONCERT

© 1988 BY ALISON BECHDEL

 O HAS ACCOMPANIED CLARICE AND TONI TO A PERFORMANCE BY A NATIONALLY KNOWN **WOMEN'S MUSICIAN** AND HER BAND....

ARE THESE WOMEN **DYKES**, OR **WHAT**?

I GUESS SO... I **DUNNO**!

SHHH!

DURING INTERMISSION....

THE AUDIENCE IS **FILLED** WITH DYKES! HOW COME THIS BAND WON'T SAY THE 'L' WORD?

MO, WHAT'S THE BIG DEAL? THEY'RE ANTI-APARTHEID,.. THEY'RE ANTI-NUCLEAR,.. THEY'RE **FEMINIST**... THEY'RE **ON OUR SIDE**!

NO THEY'RE **NOT**! IF THEY **ARE** DYKES, IT'S NOT VERY **SUPPORTIVE** OF THEM NOT TO **COME OUT**, IS IT? AND IF THEY'RE **NOT** DYKES, THEN WHO DO THEY THINK THEY **ARE**, TAKING ALL OUR HARD-EARNED **LESBIAN DOLLARS** FOR THESE WISHY-WASHY AMBIGUOUS-GENDER **LOVE** SONGS?!

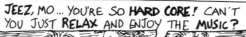

JEEZ, MO... YOU'RE SO **HARD CORE**! CAN'T YOU JUST **RELAX** AND ENJOY THE **MUSIC**?

I SHOULDA GONE TO THE **WHITNEY HOUSTON** CONCERT WITH **LOIS**.

REMEMBER, DARLING.... YOU'RE A **PACIFIST**!

NO! THESE **SEATS** ARE UNCOMFORTABLE, AND I CAN'T SEE AROUND THIS **BASKETBALL** STAR HERE!

I SWEAR THIS IS **IT**, CLARICE... I'VE BEEN VERY PATIENT BUT I HAVE MY **LIMITS**!

SATURDAY NIGHT —PART 1—

©1987 BY ALISON BECHDEL

AT LONG LAST, OUR HEROINE HAS REJOINED THE RANKS OF THE **GAINFULLY EMPLOYED.**

IT'S SATURDAY AFTERNOON AND SHE'S JUST FINISHING HER FIRST WEEK OF **CASHIERING** AT MADWIMMIN BOOKS.

ONE BUMPER STICKER, ONE SMALL CRYSTAL, ONE COPY **ON OUR BACKS**, ONE PACKAGE INCENSE... THAT'LL BE $12.49.

PHEW! QUITTIN' TIME!

12

G'NIGHT, JEZANNA! SEE YOU MONDAY!

GOOD WEEKEND, MO!

MO IS IN A PARTICULARLY GOOD MOOD BECAUSE TONIGHT IS THE FIRST BIG SOCIAL EVENT IN WEEKS... THE BENEFIT DANCE FOR THE **LESBIAN HEALTH COLLECTIVE!**

♪ OH, I WANNA DANCE WITH SOME-BODY... WANNA FEEL THE HEAT WITH SOMEBODY! ♪

OPEN

AFTER A QUICK SUPPER...

TAKEOUT LEFTOVERS

DOWN, VANESSA! EAT YER FRISKIES.

MO BEGINS HER **GROOMING RITUAL** WITH GREAT **ANTICIPATION.**

ISN'T IT **EXCITING**, GIRLS? A HOT SATURDAY NIGHT IN JULY... **ANYTHING** COULD HAPPEN!

A LITTLE **STYLING GEL** FOR THAT **WINDBLOWN** LOOK!

A LITTLE **TRIM**!

AND NOW... WHAT TO **WEAR?** SHORTS? NAH.. TOO PLAYFUL... JEANS? CAN'T GO WRONG WITH **JEANS**..

TOO **P.C.**

TOO MIAMI.

TOO **BUTCH**.

TOO **MUCH**.

FINALLY, SHE'S DRESSED...

A DISCREET **EARRING**... AND A DROP OF SANDALWOOD OIL TO ACCENTUATE MY **AURA** OF **MYSTIQUE**!

...AND ON HER WAY.

♪...WITH SOMEBODY WHO LOVES ME...♪

SPORTS

BUT **HORRORS!** IN HER **EAGERNESS**, MO HAS ARRIVED **RIGHT ON TIME!!**

NO ONE'S **HERE** YET?!?

NOPE... YOU'RE THE **FIRST!** THE D.J.'S STILL SETTIN' UP. THAT'LL BE **7** BUCKS!

STAY TUNED TO DISCOVER THE OUTCOME OF THIS MOST **AWKWARD PREDICAMENT!!**

SATURDAY NIGHT — PART 2

© 1987 BY ALISON BECHDEL

HAVING ARRIVED AT THE **BIG DANCE** UNFASHIONABLY **EARLY**, OUR HEROINE IS ENDEAVORING TO REMAIN CALM.

JUST BE COOL... PRETEND YOU **LIKE** BEING THE FIRST ONE TO ARRIVE AT A DANCE!

TESTING... TESTING...

13

EVENTUALLY, THINGS BEGIN TO PICK UP. MO **POUNCES** ON THE FIRST FAMILIAR FACE SHE SEES.

SISTERS... ARE DOIN' IT FOR THEMSELVES! ♪

HARRIET!

HI, I'M CLARICE'S FRIEND **MO**! I MET YOU AT THE **PRIDE MARCH**!

YEAH, I KNOW. NICE TO **SEE** YOU AGAIN!

SUDDENLY **NERVOUS**, MO FINDS HERSELF STRANGELY **UNABLE** TO MAKE LIGHT, FRIENDLY **CHIT-CHAT**!

SO, HOW ABOUT THESE **IRAN/CONTRA** HEARINGS?

YEAH... INCREDIBLE, HUH?

COVERT OPERATIONS! FALSE DOCUMENTS! "PLAUSIBLE DENIABILITY!" I'VE NEVER HEARD SO MANY **REVERSALS** IN MY **LIFE**! DECEPTION IS A **VIRTUE**! LAWBREAKERS ARE **PATRIOTS**! C.I.A.-BACKED MERCENARIES ARE **FREEDOM-FIGHTERS**!

WHAT CHOO WANT... BABY I GOT! ♪ WHAT CHOO NEED... YOU KNOW I GOT IT!

58

LET'S JOIN CLARICE & TONI AS THEY SPEND SOME...

"QUALITY TIME"

TOGETHER!

14

© 1987 BY ALISON BECHDEL

IT'S WEDNESDAY MORNING...

UGH! NOT AGAIN! DIDN'T WE JUST WAKE UP **YESTERDAY?**

BEEP! BEEP BEEP! BEEPBEEPBEEP!

ZNK.

CAN YOU DRIVE ME TO SCHOOL? I HAVE SOME LAST MINUTE WORK TO DO BEFORE MY **TORTS EXAM.**

OKAY, BUT HURRY UP. I'VE GOT TO DROP THE TRUCK OFF WITH THE **MECHANIC** ON MY WAY TO WORK. THE MUFFLER'S SHOT.

SKRITCH SKRITCH

CAN I BORROW SOME UNDERWEAR?

THIS IS MY **LAST PAIR!** I THOUGHT YOU WERE GOING TO DO THE **LAUNDRY** YESTERDAY!

DAMMIT! NO MILK! I **HATE** EATING DRY CEREAL!

HAVE YOU PAID THE PHONE BILL? WE GOT A FINAL NOTICE YESTERDAY.

DISCONNECTION

THE **TOAST!**

¡AY!

60

RISKY Business -part one- 15
©1987 BY ALISON BECHDEL

MO HAS JUST RUSHED OVER TO LOIS'S HOUSE TO WELCOME HER BACK FROM THE MICHIGAN WOMYN'S MUSIC FESTIVAL!

IT WAS **WILD**, MO! IT **POURED** RAIN THE WHOLE **FIVE DAYS**! I HAD **SUCH** A **GREAT TIME**!

IT SOUNDS MISERABLE

IT WAS SO **PRIMAL**! ESPECIALLY THE **MUD WRESTLING**! I FELT SO **CLOSE** TO THE **EARTH**!

MUD **WHAT**?

WRESTLING! YOU KNOW... PLAYING AND SLIDING IN THE MUD WITH A BUNCH OF **NAKED WOMEN**!

OH. RIGHT.

THAT'S WHERE I MET **KATHLEEN**! SHE ALMOST GOT ME IN A **HAMMER LOCK**, BUT I WAS TOO **SLIPPERY** FOR HER!

WE RACED TO THE SHOWERS, THEN WENT TO HER TENT AND HAD **PASSIONATE SEX** AS IT STARTED TO **POUR** AGAIN!

Panel 1: LOIS, ARE YOU MAKING THIS UP?

Panel 2: THE NEXT MORNING, I WENT TO A WORKSHOP ON "PARTHENO-GENESIS WITH GEMSTONES", WHERE I MET AMETHYST. WHAT A FASCINATING WOMAN!

DIDJA GO TO HER TENT TOO?

Panel 3: NO, SHE CAME TO MINE. Y'KNOW, I THINK SHE FOUND MY G-SPOT!

LO-IS!

COME ON, MO. SPARE ME THE PURITAN ROUTINE.

Panel 4: LOIS, YOU CAN'T JUST GO AROUND BEDDING EVERY WOMAN YOU MEET! HAVEN'T YOU HEARD? THERE'S AN EPIDEMIC GOING ON!

Panel 5: AW, MO, RELAX! LESBIANS ARE A LOW-RISK GROUP! I'M NOT GONNA GET AIDS FROM SLEEPING AROUND WITH OTHER WOMEN!

Panel 6: LOIS! BEING A DYKE DOESN'T MEAN YOU CAN'T GET AIDS! HOW DO YOU KNOW WHO ELSE ANEMONE OR ARTEMIS OR WHATEVER THE HELL HER NAME IS HAS SLEPT WITH?! YOU HAVE TO STOP HAVING SEX!!!

TO BE CONTINUED...

Panel 7: IS MO OVER-REACTING? IS LOIS UNDER-REACTING? THE DEBATE HEATS UP IN OUR NEXT EPISODE! STAY TOONED!

63

RISKY
Business
- part -
two
16
©1987 BY ALISON BECHDEL

I N OUR LAST EPISODE, WE LEFT MO AND LOIS ON THE **BRINK** OF A **DISPUTE** REGARDING LOIS'S **EROTIC EXPLOITS** IN THE FACE OF **AIDS!**

STOP HAVING SEX?! WHAT'S **WITH** YOU, MO? HAVE YOU BECOME A **FUNDAMENTALIST** SINCE I LAST SAW YOU?!

LOIS, THE REASON LESBIANS ARE **LOW-RISK** IS BECAUSE, IN GENERAL, WE DON'T HAVE A LOT OF **CASUAL SEX.** BUT **YOU** SEEM BENT ON SINGLE-HANDEDLY **REVERSING** THAT TRAIT!

THAT'S **BULLSHIT!** SINCE WHEN HAVE **YOU** BECOME AN EXPERT ON THE RATE OF CASUAL SEX IN THE LESBIAN COMMUNITY, **SISTER CELIBATE?**

L OIS'S HOUSEMATE **GINGER** STEPS INTO THE FRAY...

OOH! **LOW BLOW**, LOIS! BUT YOU **ARE** WRONG, MO. **SLEEPING AROUND** ISN'T WHAT CAUSES AIDS... IT'S A **VIRUS.**

PART OF THE REASON DYKES ARE LOW-RISK IS BECAUSE IT'S JUST **HARDER** TO **TRANSMIT** DISEASES SEXUALLY BETWEEN TWO WOMEN THAN WHEN THERE'S **SPERM** BEING ABSORBED.

THANK YOU, GINGER.

HARDER, I SAID. NOT **IMPOSSIBLE**. REMEMBER THE TIME YOU CAUGHT THE **YEAST INFECTION** FROM THAT WOMAN VISITING FOR THE **WITCHCRAFT** CONFERENCE, AND THEN **YOU** GAVE IT TO **ANGELA**?

-YEAH! SO THERE, MS. **DON JUANITA!**

HUH! I **FORGOT** ABOUT THAT... JEEZ, MAYBE I SHOULD'VE **TALKED** ABOUT THIS STUFF WITH AMARYLLIS... ER,... AMETHYST... BEFORE WE **SLEPT** TOGETHER...

I GUESS WE **ALL** GOTTA START TALKING ABOUT IT.

YEAH, **GREAT**. I HAVE A HARD ENOUGH TIME ASKING FOR A **DATE** LET ALONE GRILLING SOMEONE ON HER **SEXUAL HISTORY.**

WELL, LOOK ON THE **BRIGHT** SIDE, MO. IT GIVES YOU SOMETHING **NEW** TO WORRY ABOUT!

65

MO! I'M GLAD YOU CALLED! **WHAT'S UP**?

WHAT'S **UP**? UH... I DUNNO.. I JUST THOUGHT I'D CALL AND, UH... Y'KNOW... SEE HOW YOU **WERE**... HOW **ARE** YOU?!

ACTUALLY, AT THE MOMENT I'M KIND OF **FRUSTRATED**. I HAD THIS RIDE LINED UP FOR **THE MARCH** ON **WASHINGTON** AND IT JUST FELL THROUGH.

YEAH? WELL... GOSH, UH... Y'KNOW, YOU COULD RIDE WITH **ME**!

YEAH? DO YOU HAVE **ROOM**?

SURE! IT'S JUST ME, CLARICE, TONI AND LOIS IN LOIS'S OLD VW **BUG**! **PLENTY** OF ROOM! ...OKAY!... SO I'LL CALL YOU WITH THE DETAILS IN A COUPLE DAYS... NOT AT ALL! NICE TALKING TO **YOU TOO**! BYE!

SO, SOUNDS LIKE YOU HAVE A **DATE**.

A **DATE**? WELL, I MEAN, ALL I DID WAS OFFER HER A **RIDE**. I HOPE SHE DOESN'T THINK I'M JUST LOOKING FOR A **DATE**! I MEAN, DIDJA THINK I WAS TOO **HEAVYHANDED**? DID I SOUND LIKE I JUST WANTED TO **SLEEP** WITH HER?

IT'S GONNA BE A LONG WAY TO D.C.

67

ON THE ROAD

EN ROUTE TO THE **MARCH ON WASHINGTON,** OUR STALWART BAND OF TRAVELERS PAUSES BRIEFLY IN THE **HEARTLAND** OF **AMERICA...**

18

UGH! THIS CHILI HAS **MEAT** IN IT!

WHADJA **EXPECT** AT HOJO'S? **TEMPEH?**

I **HATE** USING THE BATHROOMS IN THESE PLACES...THIS **5-YEAR OLD** JUST ASKED HER MOTHER IF I WAS A **BOY** OR A **GIRL!**

SO? YOU SHOOK UP A LITTLE KID'S **ASSUMPTIONS.** IT WAS **GOOD** FOR HER!

YEAH. THINK OF YOURSELF AS A WALKING **EDUCATIONAL EXPERIENCE.** YOU SHOULD TRY BEING THE **FIRST BLACK PERSON** ONE OF THESE CORN-FED KIDS HAS EVER SEEN!

I DUNNO. REST STOPS GIVE ME THE CREEPS.

THESE PEOPLE LOOK LIKE **ESCAPEES** FROM **HERITAGE USA.**

69

Bringing it Home

©1987 BY ALISON BECHDEL

WELL, WE MANAGED TO SCRAPE BY WITHOUT YOU, MO. AFTER ALL, IT WAS FOR A GOOD CAUSE.

GOD, IT WAS **INCREDIBLE**, JEZ! HALF·A·MILLION OF US! WE TURNED THAT **CREEPY, IMPERIAL- IST CAPITAL** INTO A WHOLE DIFFERENT **WORLD!**

FOR **ONE WEEKEND** WE HAD A GLIMPSE OF REAL **FREEDOM**. IT WAS LIKE BEING 100% QUEER AND **PROUD** OF IT, BUT AT THE SAME TIME NOT BEING **QUEER** AT **ALL** ANYMORE... Y'KNOW?

YEAH, I **DO** KNOW. I WASN'T EVEN THERE BUT I CAN SURE FEEL THAT **ENERGY!**

MO! YOU'RE **BACK!**

HEY, LOIS! YEAH, I GOT HOME LAST NIGHT. SOME **LESBERADO WITCHES** WE WERE IN **JAIL** WITH GAVE US A RIDE IN THEIR **WINNEBAGO!**

JEZANNA, YOU WOULDN'T HAVE **RECOGNIZED** OUR **UPTIGHT LITTLE MO!** WE'RE ALL READY TO **LEAVE** AFTER THE MARCH, BUT **SHE** DECIDES TO STAY ON FOR THE **CIVIL DISOBEDIENCE!** NO RIDE HOME, NO **BAIL MONEY**, NO AFFINITY GROUP!

WELL, **HARRIET** AND I REALIZED DURING THE MARCH THAT WE REALLY HAD NO **CHOICE**... IT WAS JUST A NECESSARY THING TO DO.

HARRIET, EH? NO DOUBT THE SAME HARRIET WHOSE **PHONE NUMBER** YOU'VE BEEN **FONDLING** FOR WEEKS... SO, YOU GOT **ARRESTED**?

" YEAH... WE GOT THROUGH THE POLICE BARRICADE ON THE STEPS OF THE **SUPREME COURT** AND HAD A SYMBOLIC **KISS-IN** WITH ALL THESE **WILD WOMEN**!..."

EQUAL JUSTICE UNDER LAW

" I WAS **KISSING HARRIET** WHEN THE ARRESTING **OFFICERS** PULLED US **APART**!"

CROSS

IT WAS SO... SUCH A **REVOLUTIONARY GESTURE**!

YEAH, I'LL **BET**!

IT'S JUST WONDERFUL TO HAVE SUCH AN **EMPOWERED** EMPLOYEE, MO. NOW YOU CAN START MAKING SOME REVOLUTIONARY GESTURES WITH **THIS**.

71

BUTT REACTION

©1987 BY ALISON BECHDEL

(20)

BRUNCHING AT **CAFÉ TOPAZ**, MO HAS SHOWN ABSOLUTELY **NO INTEREST** IN CLARICE AND TONI'S DISCUSSION ABOUT **U.S. AID** TO THE **CONTRAS**...

ARE YOU **FEELING** ALL RIGHT, MO?

HUH? OH, YEAH. I'M FINE...

UH... SO, TELL ME **EVERYTHING** YOU KNOW ABOUT **HARRIET**. IS SHE **INVOLVED** WITH SOMEONE?

MO, FER **GODDESS' SAKE!** YOU SPENT A NIGHT IN **JAIL** AND DROVE HALFWAY ACROSS THE **COUNTRY** WITH HER... SURELY YOU GOT BEYOND **SMALL TALK!**

WELL... IT DOESN'T **SEEM** LIKE SHE HAS ANY PRIMARY-TYPE PERSON... SHE MENTIONED AN **EX**-LOVER, BUT SHE NEVER ACTUALLY SAID SHE WAS **AVAILABLE!**

I MEAN, WHAT IF I ASK HER ON A **DATE** DATE BUT SHE THINKS IT'S JUST A **FRIENDLY** DATE... WHAT IF I MAKE A **FOOL** OF MYSELF?!

MO, TRUST YOUR **INSTINCTS!** YOU'LL BE ABLE TO **TELL** IF SHE'S INTERESTED OR NOT!

MOMENTARILY STUNNED, OUR HEROINE QUICKLY REGAINS HER COMPOSURE.

I **SAID**, I JUST CAME BY TO SEE **YOU**.

REALLY? UH... I MEAN, UM, WE'LL BE CLOSING IN A FEW MINUTES... ARE YOU **HUNGRY?** WE COULD, UM... HAVE **DINNER?**

GREAT! I'D **LOVE** TO... I'LL BROWSE AROUND TILL YOU'RE READY.

JEZANNA! THAT'S **HER!** THAT'S **HARRIET!** SHE CAME BY TO **SEE** ME! WE'RE GOING OUT TO **DINNER!**

HUH. SHE'S DRESSED LIKE THAT FOR DINNER WITH YOU?

AW, THOSE ARE JUST HER **WORK** CLOTHES. SHE INVESTIGATES **HUMAN RIGHTS COMPLAINTS** FOR THE **STATE**... ISN'T SHE **GORGEOUS?**

I'LL CLOSE OUT, MO. GO ENJOY YOUR BIG DATE.

THANKS, JEZ! SEE YOU TOMORROW!

SO, WHAT DO YOU FEEL LIKE? ETHIOPIAN? MEXICAN? MACROBIOTIC?

HOW ABOUT THE **TOPAZ?**

BUT OF COURSE! SHALL WE?

SUSPENSE

©1987 BY ALISON BECHDEL

22

DINING AT CAFÉ TOPAZ, MO & HARRIET **APPEAR** TO HAVE FINALLY GOTTEN IT TOGETHER. BUT IS IT A **DATE**, OR IS IT JUST A **FRIENDLY DINNER?** ONLY **MORE** TIME WILL TELL...

THE **AMBIENCE** IS NOT EXACTLY **INTIMATE**...

I **SWEAR** EVERY DYKE I'VE EVER KNOWN IS HERE TONIGHT. HI, LIZA.

YEAH, JEEZ... ME TOO. HI NAOMI, GINGER.

NONETHELESS, THEY MANAGE TO SWAP **COMING-OUT** STORIES...

I THINK I FIRST REALLY **KNEW** WHEN I FELL IN LOVE WITH **JULIE ANDREWS** IN THE **SOUND OF MUSIC**. I WAS **FOUR** AT THE TIME...

AND **RELATIONSHIP HISTORIES**.

...YEAH, WE WERE TOGETHER **FIVE YEARS**, BUT WE HAD SEX I THINK **TWICE** DURING THE LAST **THREE** OF THEM.

EVENTUALLY THE CROWD GETS TO THEM.

HOW'S IT **GOING**, MO?

76

THEY DECIDE TO HAVE DESSERT AT A PLACE DOWN THE BLOCK.

IT'S REALLY SNOWING!

YOUR FEET MUST BE COLD.

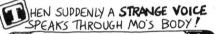

I... Y'KNOW, UM... I'M **REALLY ATTRACTED** TO YOU!

OMIGOD! WHO **SAID** THAT?!

THEN SUDDENLY A **STRANGE VOICE** SPEAKS THROUGH MO'S BODY!

THEY LINGER...

MORE TEA?

SURE.

A HORRIFYING SILENCE ENSUES. IS IT AN **HOUR**, OR MERELY SEVERAL **SECONDS**?

THUMP THUMPA THUMP

SOMEHOW, EVENTUALLY, THEIR **KNEES** TOUCH.

SIGH!

GASP!

I'VE HAD A CRUSH ON YOU FOR **MONTHS**.

THANK **GODDESS**! I WAS ABOUT TO COMMIT **HARA-KIRI** WITH MY **TEASPOON**!

MOD-ERN LOVE

23

© 1988 BY ALISON BECHDEL

AFTER DECLARING THEIR MUTUAL **ATTRACTION**, OUR HEROINES RETURN TOGETHER TO **MO'S APARTMENT** UNDER THE PRETENSE OF **WARMING** HARRIET'S **FEET**.

HARRIET HAS JUST REFUSED MORE **TEA**.

UH... LISTEN, HARRIET... I HATE TO MAKE **ASSUMPTIONS** ABOUT WHAT'S GOING **ON** HERE... BUT IN THE EVENT THAT YOU AND I, Y'KNOW... AT SOME POINT, SAY, MAYBE GOT **SEXUAL**... HYPOTHETICALLY **SPEAKING**, OF COURSE... AH... I THINK WE SHOULD TALK ABOUT WHERE WE'VE **BEEN** AND ALL, CONSIDERING **AIDS** AND EVERYTHING... Y'KNOW?

HUH! THAT WAS REALLY BRAVE OF YOU... I DIDN'T KNOW EXACTLY HOW TO BRING IT UP...

OKAY. SO, I'VE NEVER SLEPT WITH A **MAN**... NEVER DONE **I.V. DRUGS**,... NEVER HAD A **BLOOD TRANSFUSION**, ...BUT I DID ONCE HAVE A... UH... **FLING** WITH A WOMAN WHOSE **HISTORY** I WAS UNSURE OF...

A **ONE-NIGHT STAND**? A CHEAP, TAWDRY ENCOUNTER? **YOU**? MO, I'M SHOCKED!

I WAS YOUNG AND **FOOLISH**! IT WAS MY **FIRST TIME** IN A WOMEN'S BAR... I THOUGHT IT WAS **REQUIRED BEHAVIOR**! SHE **SEDUCED** ME AND I NEVER **SAW** HER AGAIN!

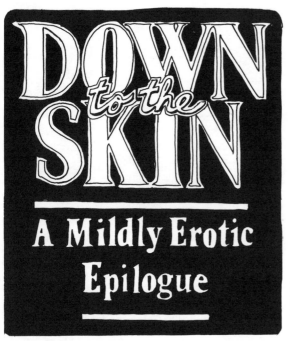

DOWN *to the* SKIN

A Mildly Erotic Epilogue

At long last, our lovelorn heroine has engaged the affections of another! But have her dormant **PASSIONS** forgotten the **WAYS** of the **GODDESS**... or will they succeed in rising, **PHOENIX-LIKE**, from the **ASHES** of her sexual **FRUSTRATION**?

87

"... AND I'VE NEVER DONE I.V. DRUGS OR HAD ANY KIND OF SEX WHERE BLOOD WAS EXCHANGED... BESIDES, WOMAN-TO-WOMAN TRANSMISSION IS REALLY RARE. WE'RE **PROBABLY** BOTH SAFE."

"YEAH.. I GUESS YOU'RE RIGHT. I JUST TEND TO **WORRY** A LOT ABOUT THINGS, Y'KNOW?"

"OH, **REALLY?** I HADN'T NOTICED."

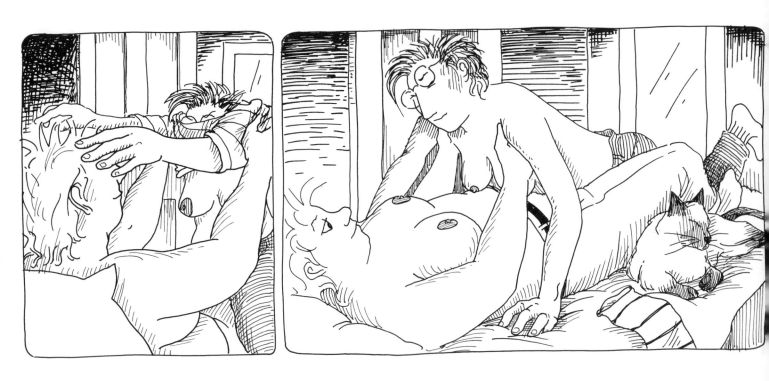

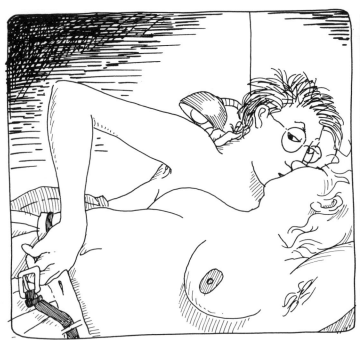
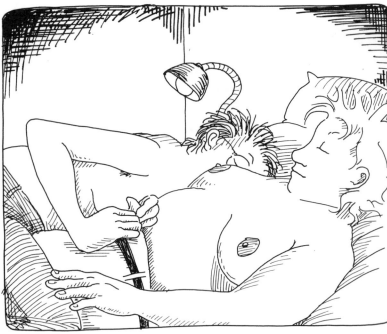

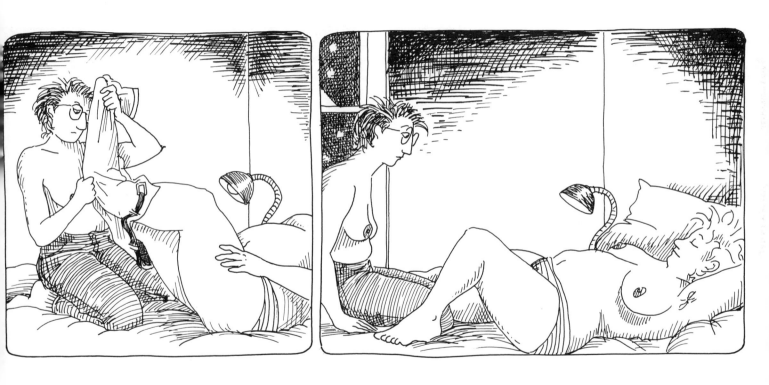

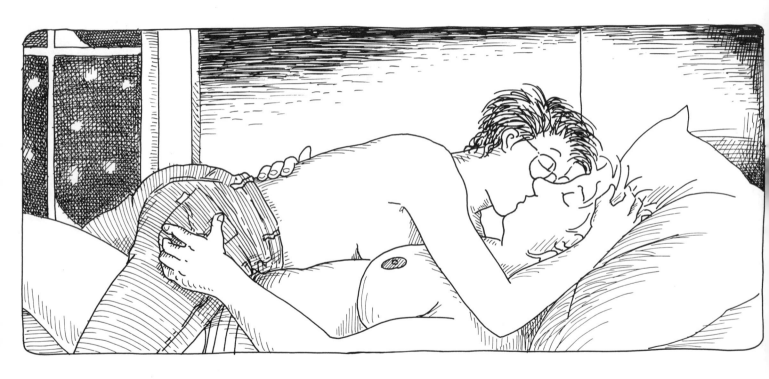

99

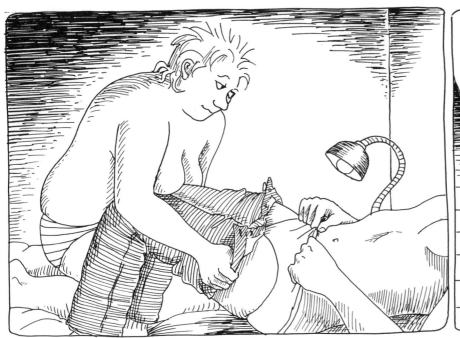

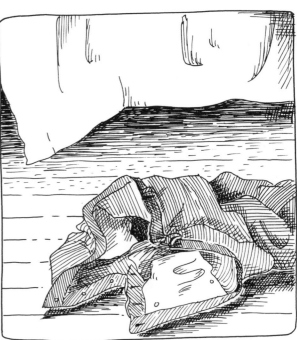

101

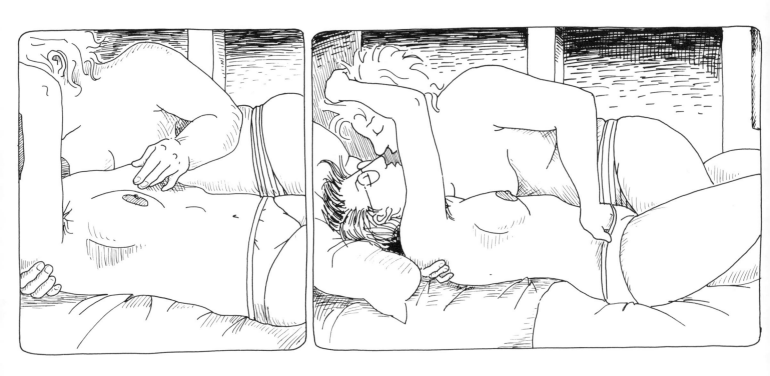

WAIT... I FEEL SILLY IN JUST MY SOCKS..

103

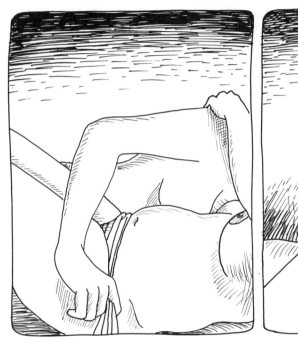

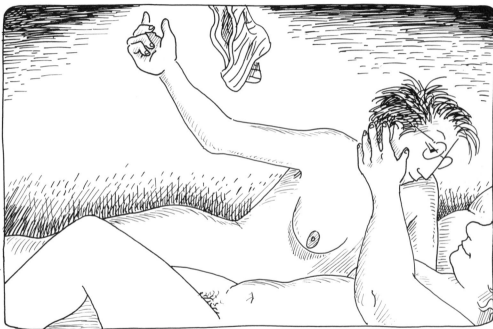

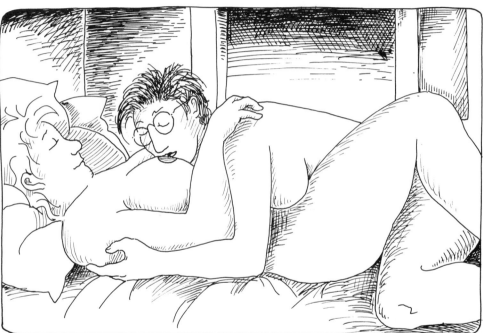

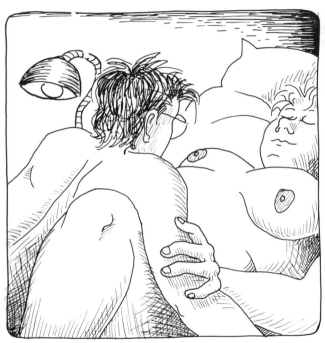
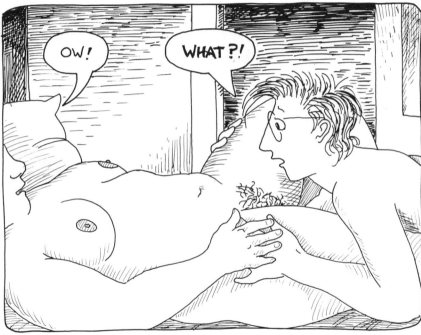

107

THUS STRIPPED OF HER EARTHLY BONDS, OUR HEROINE EMBARKS ON THE SACRED RITES OF **APHRODITE**, LEAVING US FOR **CELESTIAL SPACES** HERETOFORE ONLY APPROXIMATED BY HER **MORE DARING** FANTASIES.

Firebrand Books is an award-winning feminist and lesbian publishing house. We are committed to producing quality work in a wide variety of genres by ethnically and racially diverse authors. Now in our four-teenth year, we have over ninety titles in print.

A free catalog is available on request from Firebrand Books, 141 The Commons, Ithaca, New York 14850, 607-272-0000.

Visit our website at www.firebrandbooks.com.